WORDS & MUSIC BY PAUL WILLIAMS

Published 2001

Edited by Anna Joyce
Art Direction by Dominic Brookman
© International Music Publications Ltd
Griffin House 161 Hammersmith Road London W6 8BS England

NO PERFORMANCE MAY BE GIVEN WITHOUT A LICENCE
From time to time it is necessary to restrict or even withdraw the rights of certain musicals for production.
It is therefore vital to check availability with us well in advance before committing yourself to produce a particular
musical or beginning rehearsal, as considerable embarrassment may otherwise result.
For further information and/or an application form, please contact:

Warner/Chappell Musicals Department
Tel: 020 8563 5887
Fax: 020 8563 5801

ACT ONE

FAT SAM'S GRAND SLAM
Razamataz and the girls welcome you to Fat
Sam's Grand Slam Speakeasy.

11

BAD GUYS
Fat Sam's gang of dumb bums sing their song.

16

ACT TWO

MY NAME IS TALLULAH

Tallulah, Sam's girlfriend and the vamp of the chorus, sings her tantalising number.

SO YOU WANNA BE A BOXER

Cagey Joe gives Leroy the low down on being a champion fighter. You're nothing, if you haven't got 'it.'

RENDEZVOUS AT FOX'S DELI

I first had the idea of a gangster musical film with no adults in the cast, just kids, as far back as Christmas 1973. As most people thought I was a looney I didn't exactly get down to writing the script of Bugsy Malone until a year later.

By March 1975 the finished draft was ready and we were racking our brains for someone to do the score. It wasn't easy. We thought film musicals had moved on a bit since the hands-across-the-table bursting-into-song days and no composer suggested seemed quite right.

In desperation the Producer turned to me and said, "Well, who do *you* like?"

"My personal favourite is Paul Williams", I said, "but would he do it?" So we asked him, and he liked the idea and said he would. A week later I was on a plane to Las Vegas to talk to Paul who was performing in cabaret at The Sands.

Our first meetings were in between his twice-nightly shows and we just talked about the story and characters. "Talk" is not quite the right word as Paul would croak in a low whisper to save his voice for the late show. Needless to say for two nights we didn't get very far. By the third day we decided to have lunch and thrash it out. We drove down the main Las Vegas strip and went into a drugstore-come-restaurant called 'Fox's Deli.'

For four hours, in between Paul signing autographs and the waitress spilling coffee on my script, we went through the story, line by line, character by character, song by song.

Paul has a remarkable facility for humming a melody the moment you mention a phrase or a situation. Each tune seemed marvellous and I was terrified he would forget them, but he seems blessed with a tape recorder locked away up inside his head somewhere.

Four beef spitfires, two banana boozles, two salami specials and a lot of Coors beer later, we had the structure for the basic score. Six weeks later, Paul had written and recorded the basic tracks and we were rehearsing to music on Pinewood Studios 'H' Stage.

If you've seen the film you will know how beautifully Paul's songs fit the story. If you haven't seen Bugsy Malone just enjoy the music . . . and make sure you catch the movie as soon as you can. After all, it's not every day they get a musical written at 'Fox's Deli.'

ALAN PARKER

A GOODTIMES PRODUCTION
OF ALAN PARKER'S FILM

Bugsy Malone

THE STORY

(1929, GANGSTER WARFARE IN NEW YORK)

Dandy Dan's hoodlums terrorise the district, exterminating undesirables with their new weapon - splurge guns. His rival is Fat Sam Stacceto, who runs the Grand Slam Speakeasy, but Fat Sam's gang still use old-fashioned pies. Fat Sam engages the help of Bugsy Malone, a smooth city slicker who hitherto has been more occupied in sweet-talking Blousy Brown, a would-be singer. With Bugsy's help, Fat Sam escapes from a frame-up but he learns later that Dandy Dan's mob have splurged nearly all his gang. They've also destroyed his sarsaparilla and grocery rackets - the whole empire's gone! There's only one hope left. Fat Sam pays Bugsy $400 in exchange for more help. Bugsy, who has promised to take Blousy to Hollywood, has to break his date with her. Is she mad! Meanwhile, Bugsy and Leroy Smith, a guy with an awesome punch, witness a secret delivery of spurge guns at Dock 17. With a bunch of down-and-outs, they help themselves from the crates. Then the police arrive, led by Captain Smolsky and Lieutenant O'Dreary. Bugsy and the gang escape through a trapdoor. Finally Dandy Dan prepares for a showdown at Fat Sam's Speakeasy. When his mob burst in, Bugsy and the guys let 'em have it - the works. Splurge, custard pies, flour bombs... Out of the gooey pandemonium it emerges that Bugsy and Blousy have made it up. Peace has broken out at last.

NO PERFORMANCE MAY BE GIVEN WITHOUT A LICENCE

From time to time it is necessary to restrict or even withdraw the rights of certain musicals for production. It is therefore vital to check availability with us well in advance before committing yourself to produce a particular musical or beginning rehearsal, as considerable embarrassment may otherwise result. For further information and/or an application form, please contact:

Warner/Chappell Musicals Department
Tel: 020 8563 5887
Fax: 020 8563 5801

Instrumental parts are available for hire from Warner/Chappell Musicals Department

PRINCIPAL CHARACTERS (plus chorus)
Bugsy Malone (who also acts as occasional narrator)
Blousey Brown (his girl and would-be Hollywood singer)
Fat Sam (gangland boss and speakeasy owner)
Dandy Dan (Fat Sam's rival)
Knuckles (Fat Sam's right-hand man)
Fizzy (general factotum and singer)
Tallulah (speakeasy girl singer and Blousey's rival)
Leroy Smith (heavyweight boxing hopeful)

PRINCIPAL MUSICAL NUMBERS
Bugsy Malone (three girl singers)
Tomorrow (Fizzy)
I'm Feeling Fine (Blousey)
My Name Is Tallulah (Tallulah)
Ordinary Fool (Blousey)
Fat Sam's Grand Slam (girls)
You Give A Little Love (chorus)

INSTRUMENTATION (Total number of books = 10)
1 Clarinet I or Flute
1 Clarinet II or Alto Sax
1 Bassoon
1 Trumpet
1 Trombone
1 Guitar
1 Bass Guitar
1 Drums
1 Piano
1 Full Score

1 The Clarinet I part is for one player doubling Flute. If no such player is available, the Flute part can be played on Clarinet. The band part is written with either alternative in mind and a separate Flute can be obtained if so desired.

2 The Clarinet II part is for one player doubling Alto Sax. If no such player is available, the Alto Sax part can be played on Clarinet. The band part is written with either alternative in mind and a separate Alto part can be obtained if so desired.

Fat Sam's Grand Slam

Words and Music by Paul Williams

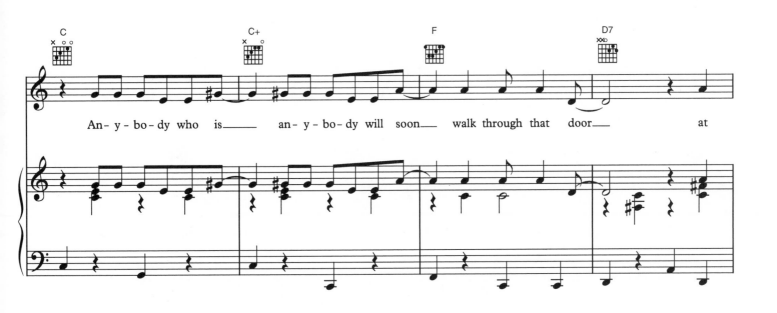

An-y-bo-dy who is____ an-y-bo-dy will soon____ walk through that door____ at

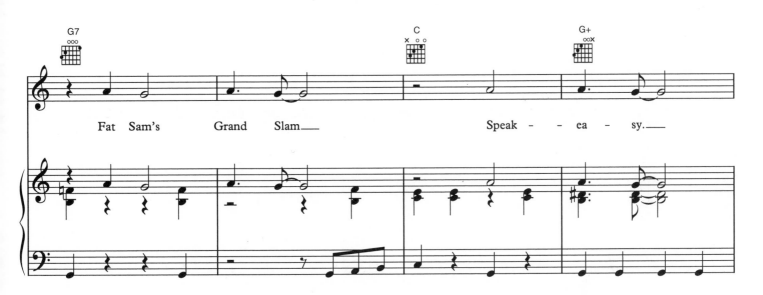

Fat Sam's Grand Slam____ Speak - - ea - sy.____

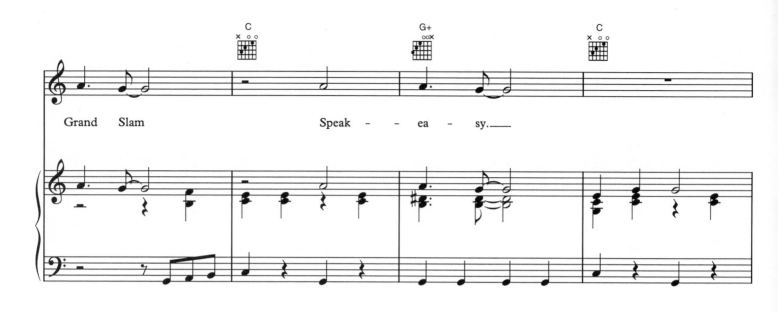

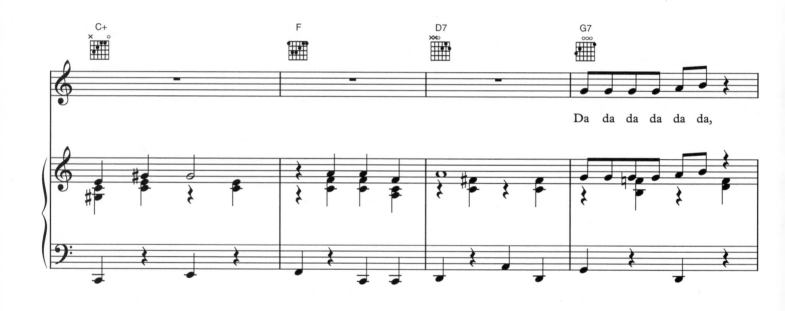

hoo ya,___ hoo da da da da,___ see the pol - i - ti -cian

D. $\text{\textsection}$ al $\oplus$ coda

sit - tin' by the kit -chen said he caught his fin - gers in the well he was wish - in'

$\oplus$ **Coda**

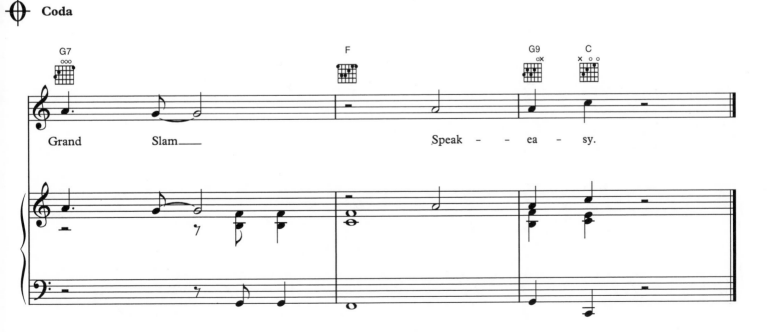

Grand Slam___ Speak - - ea - sy.

Bad Guys

Words and Music by Paul Williams

Steady 4

We could-'ve been an-y-thing that we want-ed to be,___
We could-'ve been an-y-thing that we want-ed to be,___

but don't it make your heart glad   that we de-ci-ded, a
with all the ta-lent we had   no doubt a-bout it, we

mas - tered com - plain - ing. Man - ners seemed un - nec - es - sa - ry.

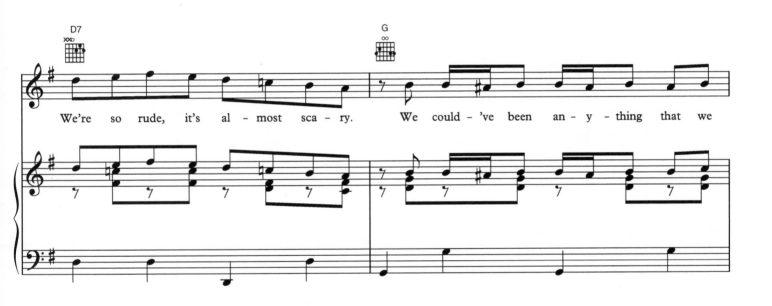

We're so rude, it's al - most sca - ry. We could - 've been an - y - thing that we

want - ed to be___ with all the ta - lent we had.___

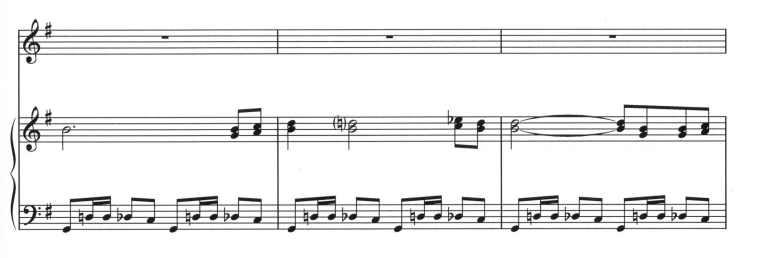

repeat and fade

repeat and fade

My Name Is Tallulah

Words and Music by Paul Williams

My name is Tal-lu-lah. My first rule of thumb___ I

don't say where I'm go-ing or where I'm com-ing from. I try to leave a lit-tle rep-u-

won't ask why.___ I've made a lot of friends in some ex - ot - ic pla - ces, I

don't re - mem - ber names but I re - mem - ber fa - ces.

Lone - ly,___ you don't have to be

No one south of Hea-ven's gon-na treat you fin-er. Tal-lu-lah had her train-ing in

to coda

North Car-o-li-na.

My name is Tal-lu-lah and soon I'll be gone,— an

So You Wanna Be A Boxer

Words and Music by Paul Williams

So you wan - na be a box - er in the gold - en ring.

Can you punch like a south - bound freight train? Tell me just one thing — can you

I've trained the best. When you work and you sweat and you bet that you train to a
not a punched-out tramp. If you lis-ten and you learn, there's an hon-our you can earn and de-

buzz-saw then you near lose your mind when you find that your boy has a
fend here. When you do see the crown, you're— king, not a clown, a con-

glass jaw. So you might as well quit if you have-n't got it.
ten-der. But you might as well quit if you have-n't got it.